Contents

A simple code tells you the level of difficulty of each Photocopy Master:

G000090426

●   Basic work

●●   For all children

●●●   Enrichment and extension

Some 'Master' sheets are included, enabling you to tailor particular activities to individual children's needs. These are coded **(M)** .

making 10

4	7	8
2	1	6
8	10	0
3	4	5
5	2	4
0	9	3
6	7	2
5	0	10

6	3	

Teacher's instructions
Matching squares on the two towers have numbers which make 10.
Write numbers in the squares of the tower on the right.

1

making 10

5	6	1	6	2	4
7	2	5	8	1	7
3	7	9	4	8	2
0	7	0	7	3	8
5	1	9	6	8	9
9	4	3	5	0	6

Teacher's instructions
A game for two players, each with a set of counters Shuffle a set of cards (without picture cards) and place them face down in a pile. Take turns to turn over the top card. Place a counter on a square whose number makes 10 with the card number. Only one counter is allowed on each square. The winner is the first one with four counters in a straight line.

Materials
Counters
Playing cards

2

Name _____

adding

12p + 4p = ☐ p   11p + 7p = ☐ p

14p + 3p = ☐ p   18p + 2p = ☐ p

17p + 1p = ☐ p   15p + 4p = ☐ p

16p + 3p = ☐ p   12p + 6p = ☐ p

13p + 5p = ☐ p   13p + 4p = ☐ p

13p + 3p = ☐ p   14p + 5p = ☐ p

3

Teacher's instructions
Add the two amounts, and write the total in each space.

Name _____

adding

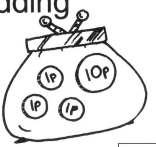

13p + ☐p = 16p

15p + ☐p = 17p

12p + ☐p = 17p

17p + ☐p = 19p

16p + ☐p = 20p

11p + ☐p = 18p

14p + ☐p = 17p

13p + ☐p = 18p

Teacher's instructions
Write the amount in each space to make the addition correct.

4

Name _____

number names

thirteen

Teacher's instructions
Count how many skittles in each set.
Write the number and number name each time.

5

number names

nine	four
thirteen	fifteen
two	twelve
twenty	one
six	eighteen
eleven	eight
three	sixteen
seventeen	five
fourteen	nineteen
seven	ten

Teacher's instructions
A game for two players, each with a set of counters.
Shuffle the number cards (I to 20), and place them face down in a pile.
Take turns to turn over the top card. Place a counter on a matching
number name. The winner is the first with five counters in any one column.

Materials
Number cards
(I to 20)
Counters

6

number names

letters		letters		letters	
eleven	6	fourteen		seventeen	
twelve		fifteen		eighteen	
thirteen		sixteen		nineteen	
				twenty	

6 letters

e l e v e n
_____ _____ _____
_____ _____ _____

7 letters

8 letters

_____ _____ _____ _____
_____ _____ _____ _____
_____ _____ _____ _____

_____ _____ _____ _____
_____ _____ _____ _____
_____ _____ _____ _____

Teacher's instructions
Count the letters in each of these number names.
Sort them into groups with equal numbers of letters by writing the names
on the bags.
Which number is not in a bag?

7

Name _____

taking away

14p – 3p = ⬜ p   16p – 2p = ⬜ p

19p – 5p = ⬜ p   13p – 1p = ⬜ p

12p – 2p = ⬜ p   17p – 3p = ⬜ p

18p – 6p = ⬜ p   19p – 7p = ⬜ p

17p – 4p = ⬜ p   14p – 4p = ⬜ p

16p – 5p = ⬜ p   18p – 5p = ⬜ p

Teacher's instructions
Complete the subtractions.

Name _____

taking away

19 − [dice: 3 spots] = 16   16 − [ ] = [ ]

17 − [ ] = [ ]   20 − [ ] = [ ]

16 − [ ] = [ ]   17 − [ ] = [ ]

18 − [ ] = [ ]   19 − [ ] = [ ]

20 − [ ] = [ ]   18 − [ ] = [ ]

Teacher's instructions
Throw a dice each time. Draw the spots and compete each subtraction.

Materials
A dice

9

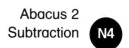
taking away from 20

14	16	15	17	19
19	17	18	15	14
15	18	16	18	16
17	15	14	16	19
14	17	19	18	14

Teacher's instructions
A game for two players, each with a set of counters.
Take turns to throw a dice. Take the dice number away from 20, and place
a counter on a square with a matching answer.
Only one counter is allowed on each square. If no square is available,
miss a turn. The winner is the first one with four counters in a straight line.

Materials
A dice
Counters

10

Name _____

taking away

$16p - \boxed{}p = 12p$

$15p - \boxed{}p = 13p$

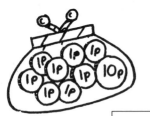

$18p - \boxed{}p = 13p$

$14p - \boxed{}p = 13p$

$17p - \boxed{}p = 14p$

$13p - \boxed{}p = 11p$

$19p - \boxed{}p = 12p$

$18p - \boxed{}p = 16p$

Teacher's instructions
Write the amount in each space to make the subtraction correct.

11

counting to 100

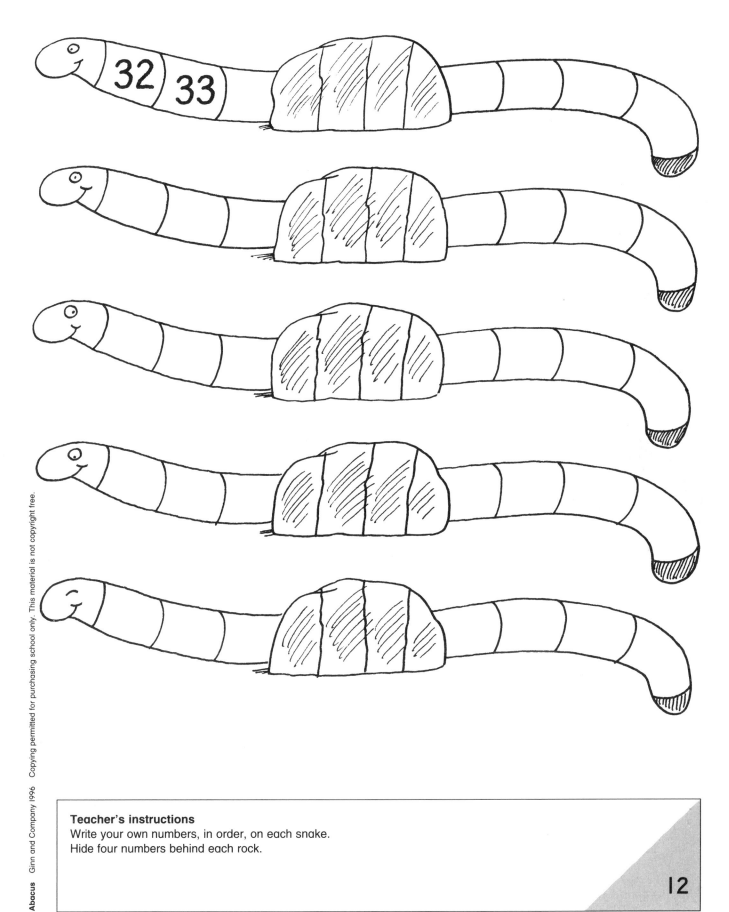

Teacher's instructions
Write your own numbers, in order, on each snake.
Hide four numbers behind each rock.

12

Name _____

numbers to 100

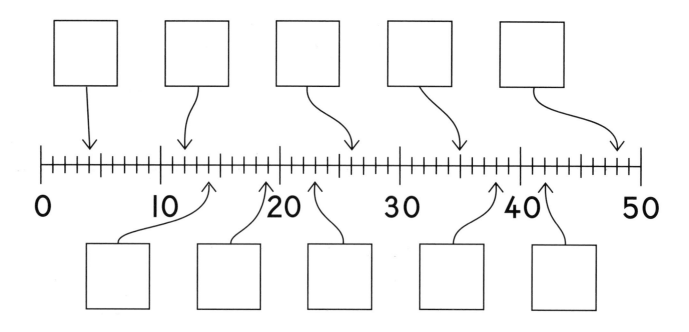

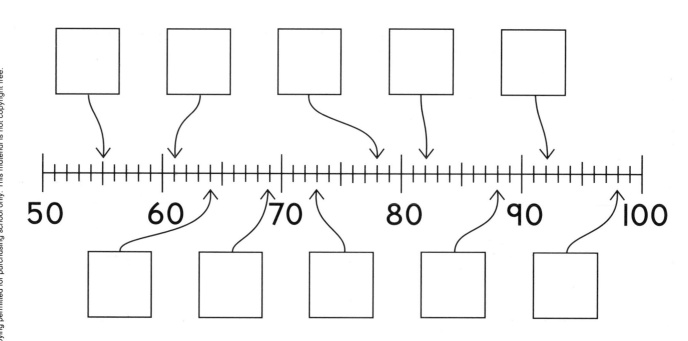

Teacher's instructions
Each arrow points to a number on the number line.
Write the number in the box each time.

13

Name _____

numbers to 100

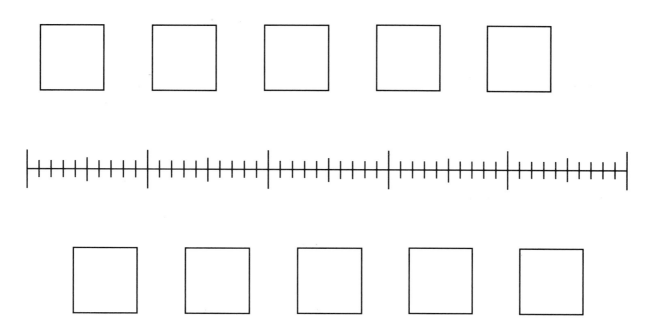

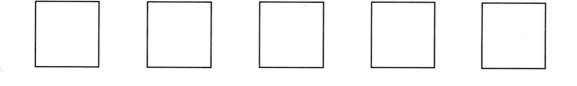

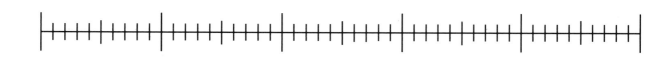

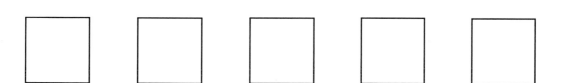

Teacher's instructions
(Teacher/pupil input: Label the large divisions on each number line.
Draw a pointer from each box.)
Write the number in the box each time.

14

Name _____

adding three numbers

3	1	6	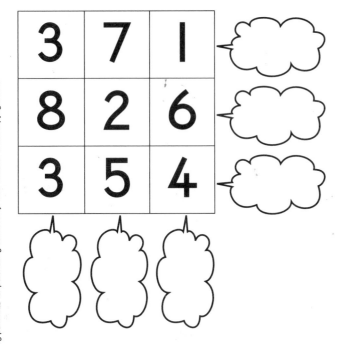
5	7	2	
8	4	3	

8	5	3
2	7	2
1	4	6

3	7	1
8	2	6
3	5	4

3	6	2
8	1	5
9	7	4

Teacher's instructions
Add the numbers in each row and each column.
Write the totals in the bubbles.

15

Name _____

adding three numbers

$3 + 4 + \boxed{} = 12$ $6 + 3 + \boxed{} = 10$

$2 + 6 + \boxed{} = 15$ $7 + 4 + \boxed{} = 13$

$5 + 3 + \boxed{} = 10$ $8 + 5 + \boxed{} = 16$

$4 + 1 + \boxed{} = 11$ $9 + 6 + \boxed{} = 19$

$3 + 7 + \boxed{} = 18$ $8 + 8 + \boxed{} = 19$

$2 + 9 + \boxed{} = 15$ $4 + 5 + \boxed{} = 15$

Teacher's instructions
Write a number in each space to make the addition correct.

16

Name _____

adding three numbers

making 10

$1 + 1 + 8 = 10$ $2 + 2 + 6 = 10$

$1 + 2 + 7 = 10$ $2 + 3 + 5 = 10$

$1 + 3 + 6 = 10$ $\boxed{} + \boxed{} + \boxed{} = 10$

$1 + 4 + 5 = 10$ $\boxed{} + \boxed{} + \boxed{} = 10$

making 9

$\boxed{} + \boxed{} + \boxed{} = 9$ $\boxed{} + \boxed{} + \boxed{} = 9$

$\boxed{} + \boxed{} + \boxed{} = 9$ $\boxed{} + \boxed{} + \boxed{} = 9$

$\boxed{} + \boxed{} + \boxed{} = 9$ $\boxed{} + \boxed{} + \boxed{} = 9$

$\boxed{} + \boxed{} + \boxed{} = 9$

Teacher's instructions
Find two more different ways of making 10.
Find seven different ways of making 9.
Investigate different ways of making other numbers.

Name

tens and ones

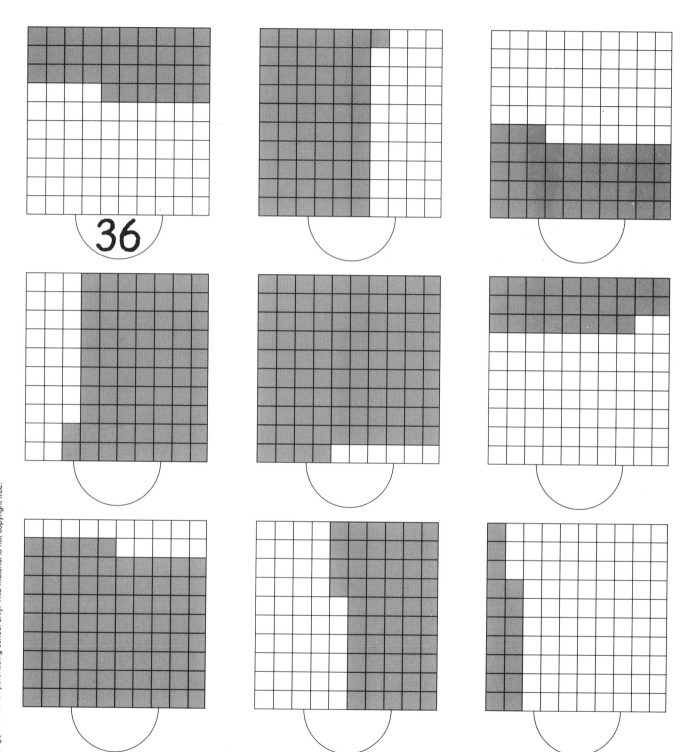

Teacher's instructions
Write down the number of shaded squares in each grid.
How many squares are not shaded in each grid?

18

Name _____

tens and ones

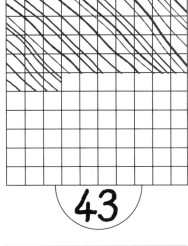

43

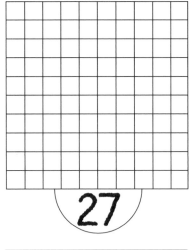

27

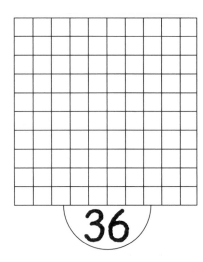

36

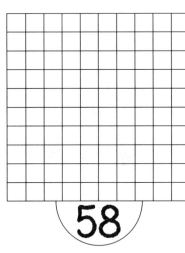

58

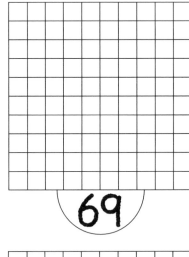

69

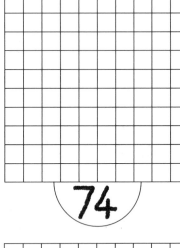

74

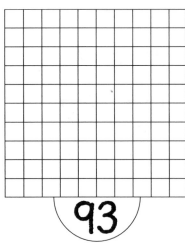

93

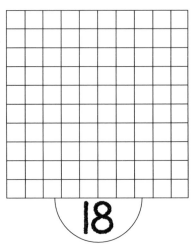

18

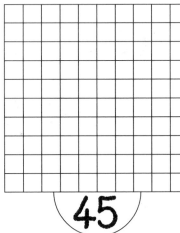

45

Teacher's instructions
Colour strips of squares and single squares to match each number.

19

adding

24 + 5 = ☐   18 + 5 = ☐

35 + 4 = ☐   26 + 3 = ☐

23 + 3 = ☐   43 + 4 = ☐

37 + 2 = ☐   38 + 3 = ☐

42 + 5 = ☐   27 + 6 = ☐

Teacher's instructions
Write the answer to each addition in the space.

20

Name _____

adding

24 + ☐ = 27   33 + ☐ = 39

41 + ☐ = 45   23 + ☐ = 28

52 + ☐ = 57   35 + ☐ = 39

44 + ☐ = 46   38 + ☐ = 43

27 + ☐ = 31   16 + ☐ = 19

36 + ☐ = 42   45 + ☐ = 50

Teacher's instructions
Write a number in each space to make the addition correct.

Name _____

taking away 6

67	32	58
21	86	93
73	56	65
44	23	43
92	76	34
35	68	71
84	95	24
50	49	88

61	26	

Teacher's instructions
Take away 6 from each number on the left-hand tower.
Write the answer in the matching square on the right-hand tower.

22

Name _____

taking away

$23 - 6 = \boxed{}$

$27 - 9 = \boxed{}$

$22 - 6 = \boxed{}$

$25 - 9 = \boxed{}$

$21 - 6 = \boxed{}$

$22 - 7 = \boxed{}$

$25 - 7 = \boxed{}$

$24 - 7 = \boxed{}$

$22 - 5 = \boxed{}$

$24 - 6 = \boxed{}$

$24 - 9 = \boxed{}$

$23 - 7 = \boxed{}$

$21 - 5 = \boxed{}$

$23 - 5 = \boxed{}$

$20 - 5 = \boxed{}$

$25 - 8 = \boxed{}$

23

Teacher's instructions
Complete the subtractions. Colour all the balloons.
If they have the same answer, make them the same colour.

Name _____

counting in twos

1	2	3	4	5	6	7	8	9	10
11	12	13	14	15	16	17	18	19	20

1	2	3	4	5
6	7	8	9	10
11	12	13	14	15
16	17	18	19	20

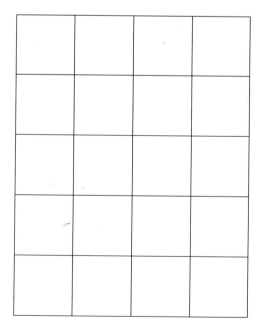

Teacher's instructions
Colour the multiples of two in each grid.
Write numbers in order from 1 to 20 on the last grid, and colour the
multiples of two.

24

Name _____

even and odd

9	35	23	17
15	14	48	16
11	35	13	49
12	34	22	7
27	15	29	55

57	9	43	7
16	42	4	3
48	8	36	31
54	34	60	65
18	32	20	19

16	4	32	17
44	11	63	15
8	56	18	10
68	17	19	82
14	90	6	20

20	56	12	40
51	33	37	14
36	52	20	48
17	9	45	32
44	28	60	16

Teacher's instructions
Colour pink the odd numbers in the top two grids.
What numbers do the pink shapes show?
Colour blue the even numbers in the bottom two grids.
What numbers do the blue shapes show?

25

Name _____

sorting

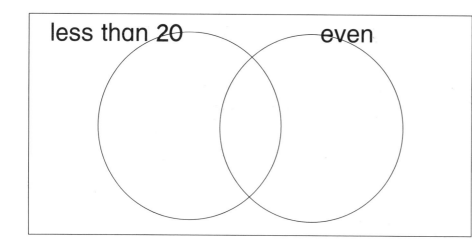

less than 20   even

11
14   6
    24
25   28
17 21
    9
18 30

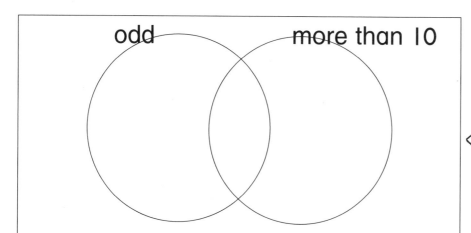

odd   more than 10

13   6
5   16
19   7
    21
20   12
  2

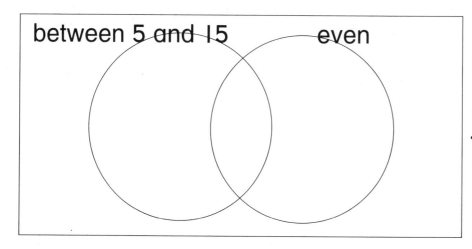

between 5 and 15   even

9
10   3
    8
11   4
  14
17   13
  2

Teacher's instructions
Write the numbers in the correct part of each diagram.

26

Name _____

sorting

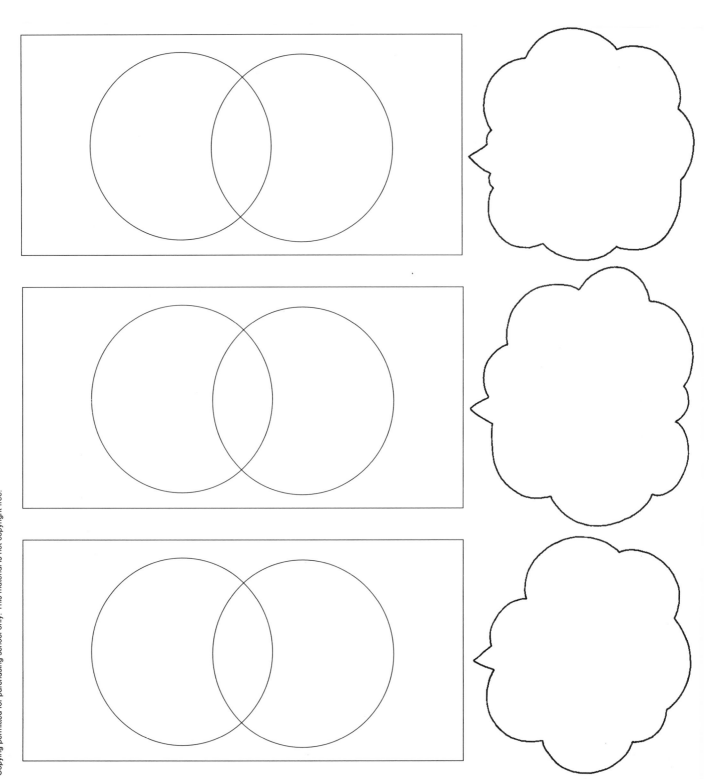

27

Teacher's instructions
(Teacher/pupil input: Write numbers in the bubbles and label the circles.)
Write the numbers in the correct part of each diagram.

adding

34 + 12 = ☐

27 + 12 = ☐

46 + 11 = ☐

39 + 10 = ☐

26 + 10 = ☐

28 + 11 = ☐

32 + 13 = ☐

41 + 13 = ☐

45 + 12 = ☐

50 + 12 = ☐

Teacher's instructions
Write the answer to each addition in the space.

sorting

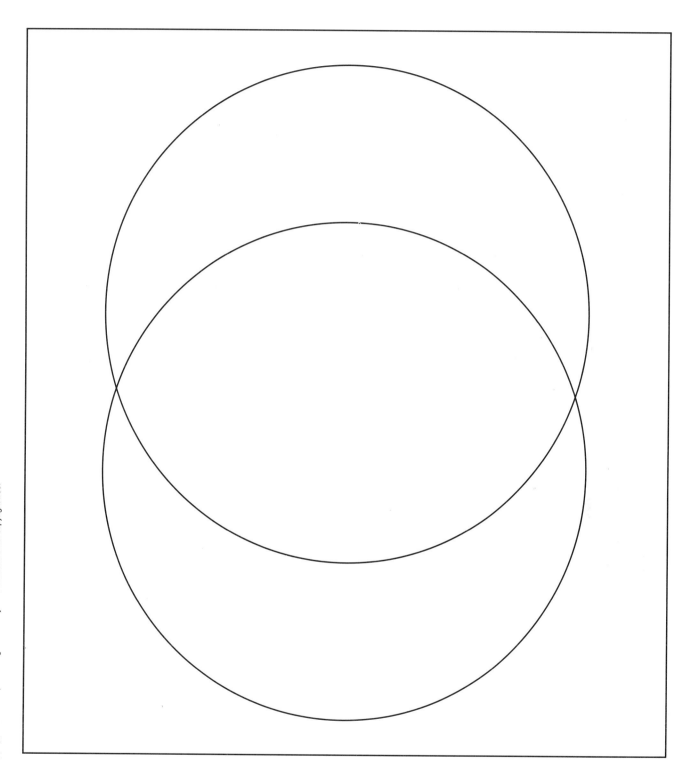

Teacher's instructions
(Teacher/pupil input: Sort selections of objects according to your own
sorting rules.)

Name _____

tens

| 20 | 60 | 90 | 10 | 40 | 70 |

10 more

| | | | | | |

| 50 | 90 | 40 | 70 | 20 | 110 |

10 less

| | | | | | |

Teacher's instructions
Write the numbers that are 10 more and 10 less in the bottom spaces.

Name _____

tens

1	2	3	4	5	6	7	8	9	10
11	12	13							20
									30
									40
									50
									60
									70
									80
									90
									100

Teacher's instructions
A game for two players, each with a different coloured pen. Split the pack of cards (without tens and picture cards) into two face-down piles (red cards and black cards). The red cards represent tens and the black cards represent units. Take turns to reveal the top card from each pile. Read the two-digit number and write it in the correct space on the grid. Continue reshuffling the cards if necessary, until one row or column is complete. The winner is the one who completes it.

Materials
Playing cards
Coloured pens

30

adding

34 + 12 = ☐

27 + 12 = ☐

46 + 11 = ☐

39 + 10 = ☐

26 + 10 = ☐

28 + 11 = ☐

32 + 13 = ☐

41 + 13 = ☐

45 + 12 = ☐

50 + 12 = ☐

Teacher's instructions
Write the answer to each addition in the space.

adding

14	23	36	21	32
46	67	18	47	65
73	5	54	72	58

add
12

→

26	35			

13	25	46	37	52
24	35	52	43	11
61	46	83	54	37

add
13

→

24	12	33	41	52
61	32	53	84	23
14	43	51	62	75

add
15

→

Teacher's instructions
Add on to the numbers on the left and write the answers in the boxes on
the right.

32

Name _____

nearest 10

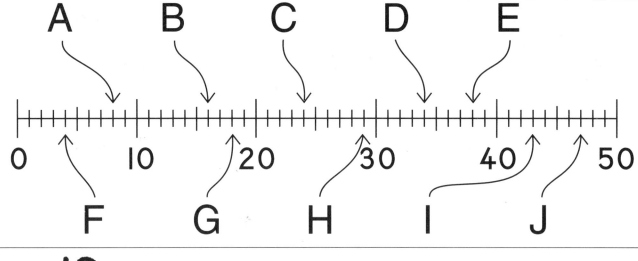

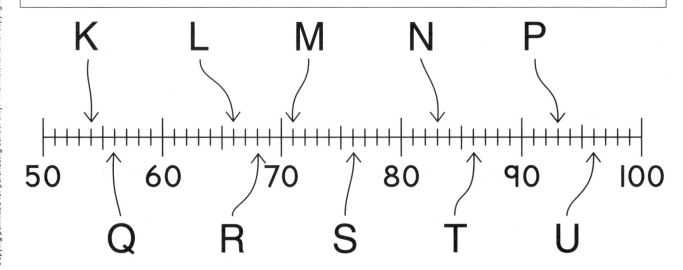

Teacher's instructions
What is the nearest 10 to the position of each letter?
Write the answer in each space.

Name _____

nearest 10

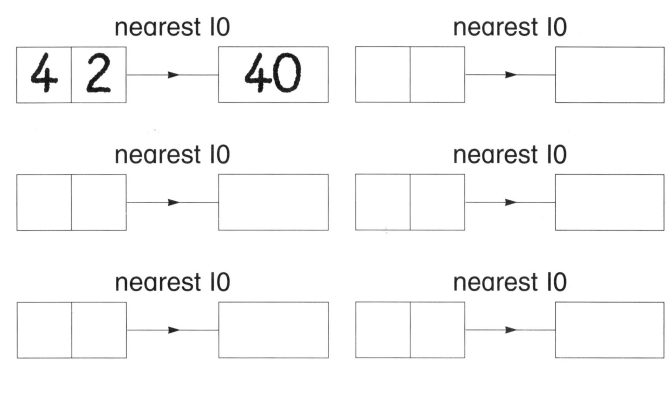

nearest 10

| 4 | 2 | → | 40 |

nearest 10

nearest 10

nearest 10

nearest 10

nearest 10

nearest 10

nearest 10

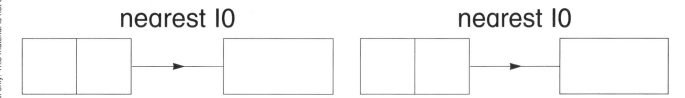

nearest 10

nearest 10

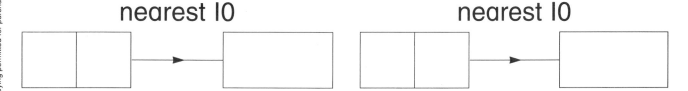

nearest 10

nearest 10

Teacher's instructions
Use four cards numbered 4, 2, 8 and 7.
Place any two cards together to make two-digit numbers.
Can you make 12 different two-digit numbers? Write them in the spaces.
Write the nearest 10 to each.

Materials
Number cards
(2,4,7,8)

34

Name _____

nearest 10

nearest 10

nearest 10

nearest 10

nearest 10

nearest 10

35

Teacher's instructions
A game for two players, each with a different coloured pen. Shuffle a pack of cards (without tens and picture cards) and place them face down in a pile. Take turns to pick two cards and arrange them to make a two-digit number. If possible, write the number alongside its nearest 10. Continue until all the spaces have been filled. The winner is the one who has written the most numbers.

Materials
Playing cards
Coloured pens

Name _____

 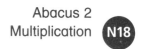
fives and tens

start

1	2	3	4	5	6	7	8
16	15	14	13	12	11	10	9
17	18	19	20	21	22	23	24
32	31	30	29	28	27	26	25
33	34	35	36	37	38	39	40
48	47	46	45	44	43	42	41
49	50	51	52	53	54	55	56
64	63	62	61	60	59	58	57

finish

Teacher's instructions
A game for two players. Each place a counter at 'start'.
Take turns to throw a dice and move your counter a matching number of
spaces. If you land on a 'five', move to the next 'five'.
If you land on a 'ten', move to the next 'ten'.
The winner is the first to reach 'finish'.

Materials
A dice
Counters

36

Name _____

fives and tens

☐ x 5 = 15

☐ x 5 = 30

☐ x 5 = 25

☐ x 5 = 5

☐ x 5 = 45

☐ x 5 = 0

☐ x 5 = 35

☐ x 5 = 50

☐ x 5 = 10

☐ x 5 = 20

☐ x 5 = 40

☐ x 10 = 20

☐ x 10 = 50

☐ x 10 = 90

☐ x 10 = 10

☐ x 10 = 70

☐ x 10 = 100

☐ x 10 = 40

☐ x 10 = 80

☐ x 10 = 30

☐ x 10 = 0

☐ x 10 = 60

Teacher's instructions
Write the missing number in each space.

37

Name _____

sharing

shared between 2

shared between 3

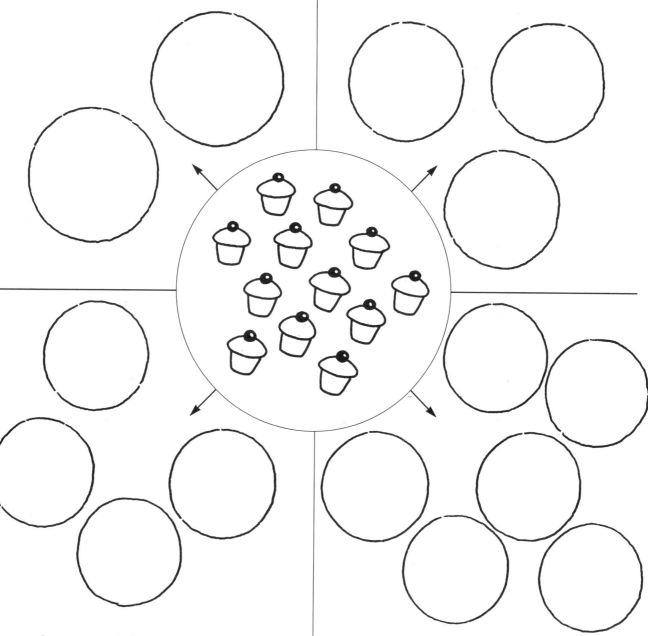

shared between 4

shared between 6

Teacher's instructions
Draw the cakes on the plates to share them equally.

Name _____

sharing

I tower	2 towers
3 towers	4 towers

Teacher's instructions
Build this tower. Build two more the same.
Use the first tower to make two smaller towers. Draw them.
Use the second tower to make three smaller towers. Draw them.
Use the third tower to make four smaller towers. Draw them.

Materials
Interlocking cubes

Name _____

differences

Teacher's instructions
A game for two players, each with a set of counters.
Take turns to throw a dice. Find two numbers whose difference matches
the dice number. Place a counter on each.
Only one counter is allowed on each circle.
The winner is the first one to place 12 counters.

Materials
A dice
Counters

40

Name _____

differences

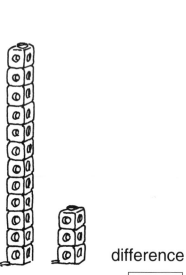

15   7   difference

16   9   difference

18   9   difference

12   3   difference

17   10   difference

20   10   difference

Teacher's instructions
Write the difference in the space each time.

Name _____

sorting

Teacher's instructions
(Teacher/pupil input: Sort selections of objects according to your own
sorting rules.)

Name _____

block graph

title:

9					
8					
7					
6					
5					
4					
3					
2					
1					

Teacher's instructions
(Teacher/pupil input: Label the columns along the bottom and draw your block graph.)

43

Name _____

block graph

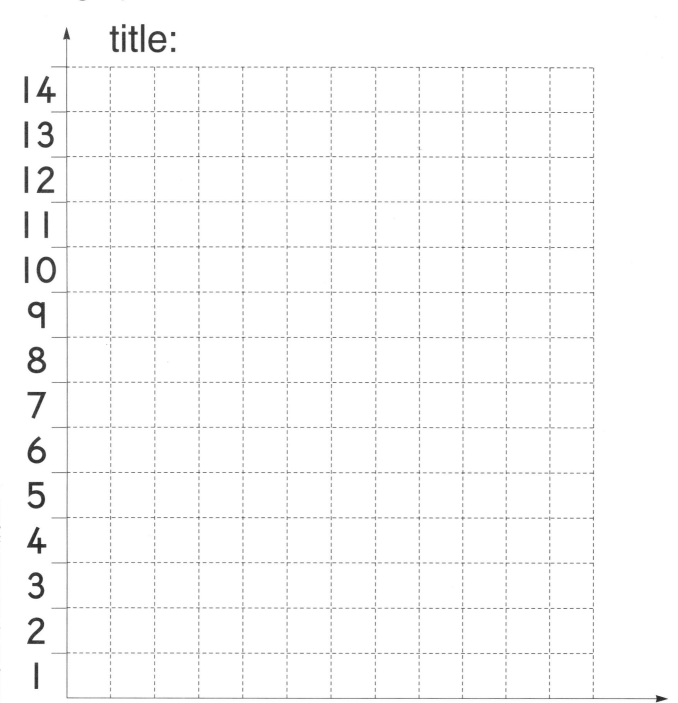

title:

14
13
12
11
10
9
8
7
6
5
4
3
2
1

Teacher's instructions
(Teacher/pupil input: Label the columns along the bottom and draw your
block graph.)

44

adding

28	46	71
15	73	39
62	32	17
53	80	68

add
―――
20

48		

32	53	41
16	9	5
25	46	69
62	70	37

add
―――
30

Teacher's instructions
Write numbers in the squares of the towers on the right.

45

adding

17p + ☐p = 27p

32p + ☐p = 62p

25p + ☐p = 55p

79p + ☐p = 99p

41p + ☐p = 81p

50p + ☐p = 80p

54p + ☐p = 84p

16p + ☐p = 66p

74p + ☐p = 94p

57p + ☐p = 67p

60p + ☐p = 90p

23p + ☐p = 63p

Teacher's instructions
Write the missing number in each space.

Name _____

adding

→ $\boxed{52}$ + 21 = $\boxed{73}$

→ $\boxed{}$ + 32 = $\boxed{}$

→ $\boxed{}$ + 23 = $\boxed{}$

→ $\boxed{}$ + 34 = $\boxed{}$

→ $\boxed{}$ + 42 = $\boxed{}$

→ $\boxed{}$ + 31 = $\boxed{}$

Teacher's instructions
Throw two dice. Put them side by side to make a two-digit number.
Draw the spots, write the number and complete the addition.

Materials
Two dice

Name _____

taking away

24 – 11 = ⬜   44 – 12 = ⬜

33 – 12 = ⬜   36 – 13 = ⬜

46 – 13 = ⬜   34 – 11 = ⬜

37 – 12 = ⬜   27 – 13 = ⬜

25 – 13 = ⬜   42 – 12 = ⬜

28 – 11 = ⬜   26 – 11 = ⬜

Teacher's instructions
Write the answer to each subtraction in the space.

48

Name _____

taking away

 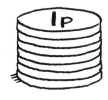 36p – 12p = ☐ p

  43p – 11p = ☐ p

27p – 13p = ☐ p

 38p – 13p = ☐ p

24p – 12p = ☐ p

Teacher's instructions
Write the answer to each subtraction in the space.

Name _____

halves and quarters

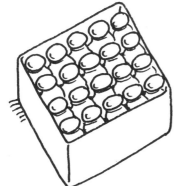

one half of ☐ is ☐

one quarter of ☐ is ☐

one half of ☐ is ☐

one quarter of ☐ is ☐

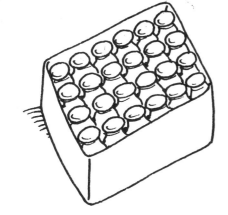

one half of ☐ is ☐

one quarter of ☐ is ☐

one half of ☐ is ☐

one quarter of ☐ is ☐

Teacher's instructions
Colour the bottles.
In each crate, colour one half red and one quarter blue.
Write how many.

50

Name _____

halves and quarters

$\frac{1}{2}$ of 10 = ☐ $\frac{1}{4}$ of 8 = ☐

$\frac{1}{4}$ of 12 = ☐ $\frac{1}{2}$ of 8 = ☐

$\frac{1}{2}$ of 6 = ☐ $\frac{1}{4}$ of 20 = ☐

$\frac{1}{4}$ of 24 = ☐ $\frac{1}{2}$ of 12 = ☐

$\frac{1}{4}$ of 16 = ☐ $\frac{1}{2}$ of 16 = ☐

$\frac{1}{2}$ of 14 = ☐ $\frac{1}{4}$ of 28 = ☐

Teacher's instructions
Use counters to help you complete these sentences.

Materials
Counters

51

Name _____

numbers to 200

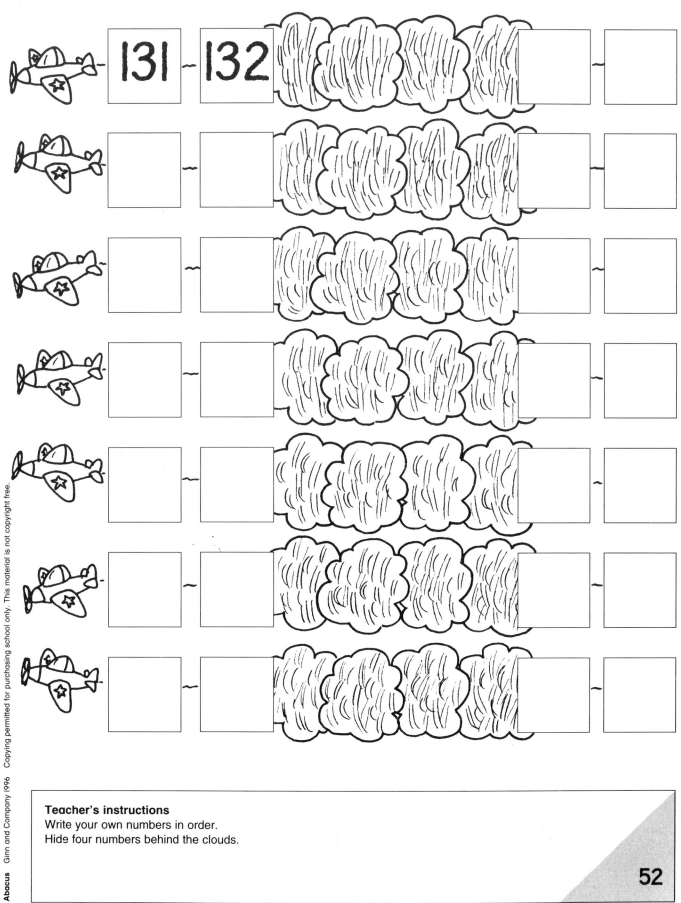

Teacher's instructions
Write your own numbers in order.
Hide four numbers behind the clouds.

52

numbers to 200

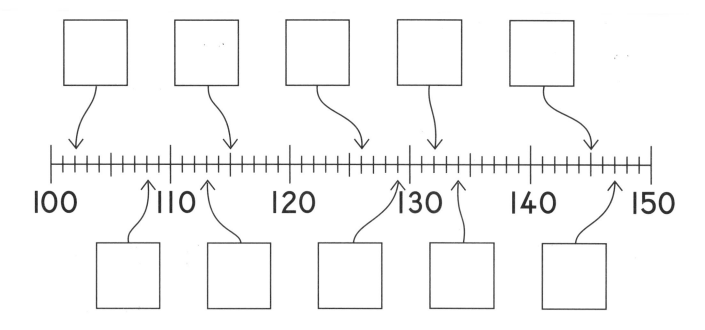

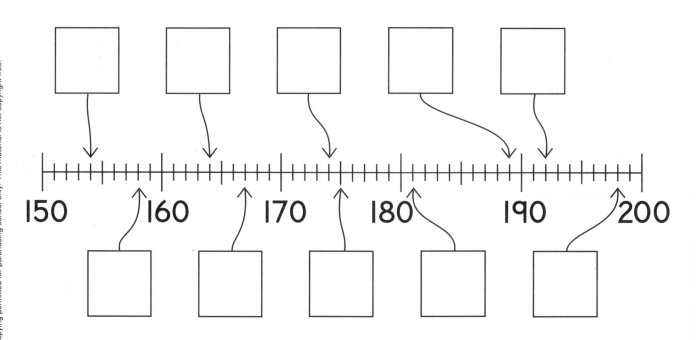

Teacher's instructions
Each arrow points to a number on the number line.
Write the number in the box each time.

53

Name _____

numbers to 200

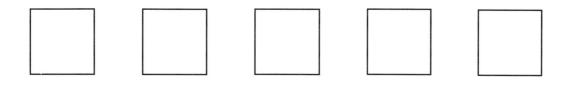

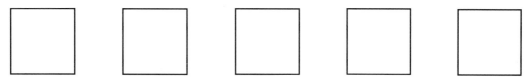

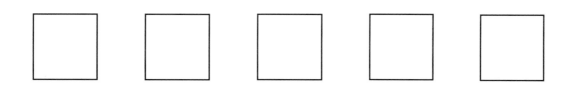

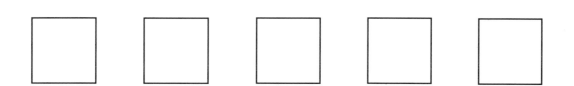

Teacher's instructions
(Teacher/pupil input: Label the large divisions on each number line.
Draw a pointer from each box.)
Write the number in the box each time.

54

Name _____

in order

	smaller	larger	points
round 1			____
round 2			____
round 3			____
round 4			____
round 5			____
round 6			____
round 7			____
round 8			____

total score

55

Teacher's instructions
A game for two or more players, each with a copy of this scoresheet.
For each round, a dice is thrown six times. After each throw, write the
number in one of your six boxes. The groups of boxes create three-digit
numbers. Once written, a number cannot be moved. Score two points if
the two three-digit numbers are in order: smaller, larger. Otherwise, score
one point. The winner is the one with the most points after eight rounds.

Materials
A dice

Name _____

 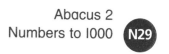

between

	smaller	between	larger	points
round 1				
round 2				
round 3				
round 4				
round 5				
round 6				

total score

Teacher's instructions
A game for two or more players, each with a copy of this scoresheet.
For each round, a dice is thrown nine times. After each throw, write the
number in one of your nine boxes. The groups of boxes create three-digit
numbers. Once written, a number cannot be moved. Score two points if the
three three-digit numbers are in order: smaller, between, larger. Otherwise,
score one point. The winner is the one with the most points after six rounds.

Materials
A dice

56

Name _____

numbers to 1000

241p

123p

312p

435p

156p

Teacher's instructions
Use £1, 10p and 1p coins.
Place coins in each purse to match the amount on the label.

Materials
Coins

Name _____

numbers to l000

Teacher's instructions
Use a pack of number cards (0 to 9). Turn the sheet on its side.
Shuffle the cards and deal out three.
Place the cards on the sheet to make different three-digit numbers.
Write them down. Then write them in order from smallest to largest.
Try with a different set of three cards.

Materials
Number cards
(0 to 9)

58

Name _____

making 50p

 3 coins   20p 10p 5p

4 coins   20p 10p 5p

4 coins 20p 10p 5p

5 coins   20p 10p 5p

5 coins  20p 10p 5p

6 coins   20p 10p 5p

6 coins   20p 10p 5p

Teacher's instructions
Colour the correct number of coins to make 50p each time.
Each line must be different.

Name _____

making one pound

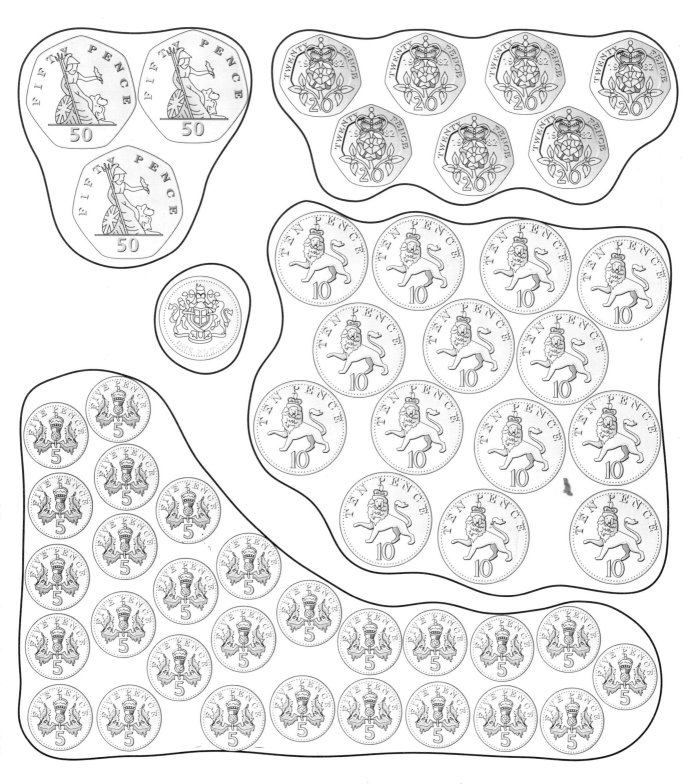

Teacher's instructions
Colour the correct number of coins in each set to make £1.

Name _____

change

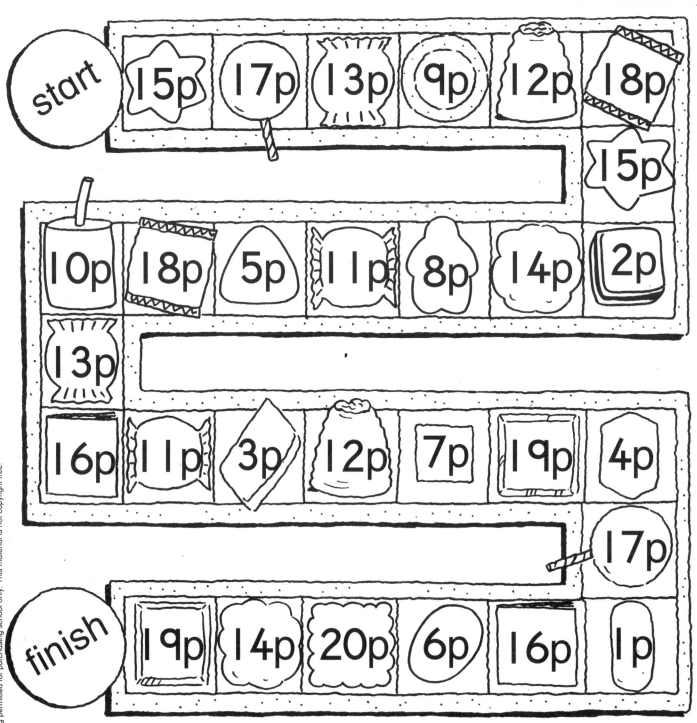

Teacher's instructions
A game for three or more players. You each need ten 20p coins. Each place a counter at 'start'. One player is 'shopkeeper' with a bank of 1p, 2p, 5p and 10p coins. Take turns to throw the dice, and move your counter forward a matching number of spaces. Buy the item you land on by paying and collecting the change. Continue until all the players have reached 'finish'. The winner is the one with the most money left.

Materials
A dice
Coins
Counters

61

Name _____

centimetres

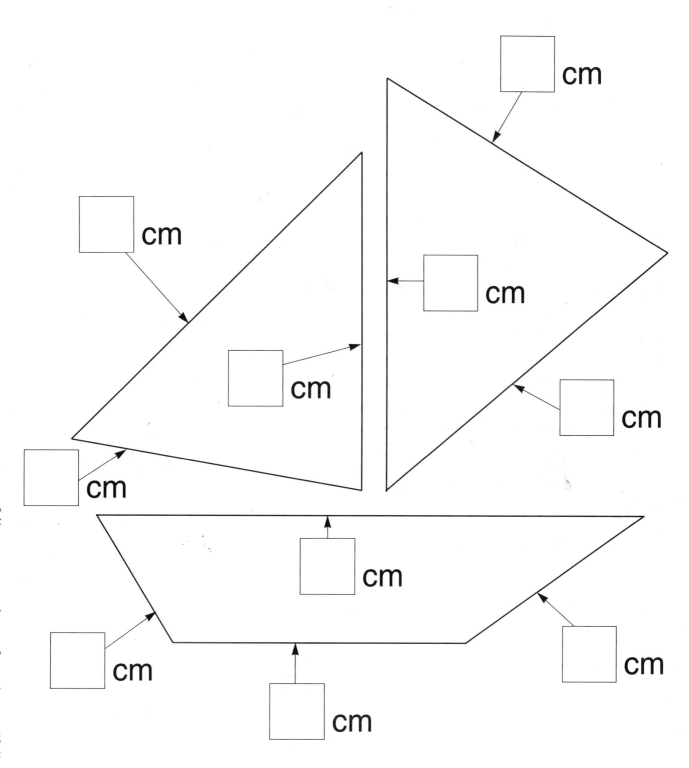

Teacher's instructions
Use a ruler to measure the length of each straight line in centimetres.
Write the lengths in the spaces.

Materials
A ruler

62

centimetres

pencil	guess	measure	difference
A			
B			
C			
D			
E			
F			
		total	

Teacher's instructions
Guess, then measure the length of each pencil.
Complete the table and find the differences.

Materials
A ruler

Name _____

decimetres

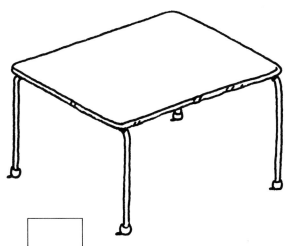

□ decimetres long

□ decimetres wide

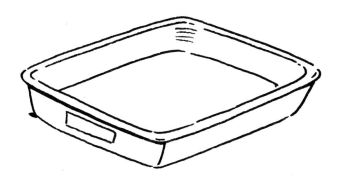

□ decimetres long

□ decimetres wide

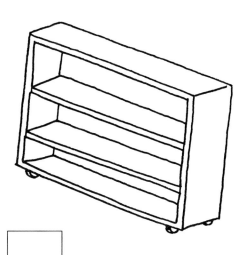

□ decimetres long

□ decimetres wide

□ decimetres long

□ decimetres wide

Teacher's instructions
Find one of each object in the pictures.
Use decimetre sticks to measure the length and width of each.

Materials
Decimetre sticks

grams

weighs 100g

weighs 200g

weighs 300g

weighs 400g

Teacher's instructions
Use a balance and some 100 gram weights.
Find an object which weighs the amount shown and draw it.

Materials
A balance
100 gram weights

Name _____

litres

☐ litres

☐ litres

☐ litres

☐ litres

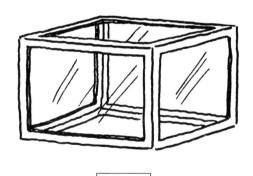

☐ litres

☐ litres

Teacher's instructions
You need a one-litre measure, and some water.
Find one of each container in the pictures.
Count how many litres you need to fill each container.

Materials
A one litre measure
Water

66

Name _____

quarter past, quarter to

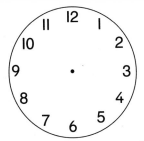

quarter past 1

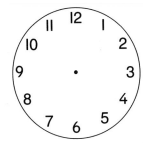

quarter past 7

quarter past 5

quarter to 3

quarter past 4

quarter to 7

quarter to 2   quarter past 6   quarter past 10

quarter past 8

quarter to 1

quarter to 11

Teacher's instructions
Draw the hands on each clock to match the time underneath.

Name _____

quarter past, quarter to

```
3.15
```

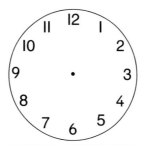

```
7.15
```

```
2.45
```

```
5.45
```

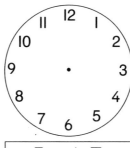

```
4.15
```

```
3.45
```

```
10.15
```

```
7.45
```

```
6.15
```

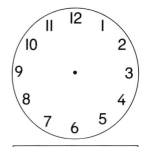

```
8.45
```

```
9.15
```

```
11.45
```

Teacher's instructions
Draw the hands on each clock to match the time underneath.

Name _____

minutes past the hour

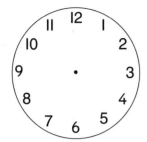

10.

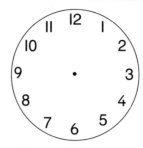

25

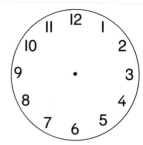

40

20

5

50

35

55

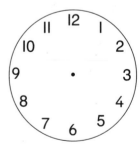

45

Teacher's instructions
Draw the position of the big hand each time to show the number of minutes past the hour.

Name _____

corners

| 2 corners | 3 corners | 4 corners | 5 corners | 6 corners |

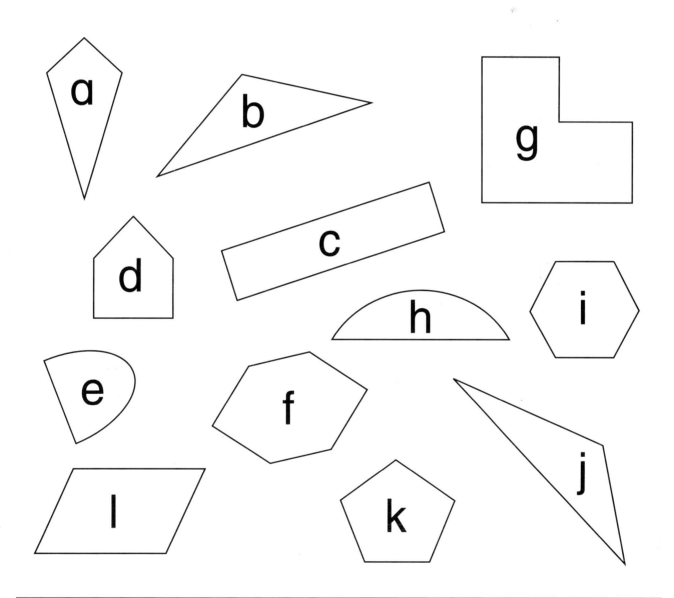

Teacher's instructions
Write the letters in the correct boxes.
Some boxes will have more than one letter.

70

Name _____

sides

71

Teacher's instructions
Colour the shapes:
　　blue if they have three sides
　　red if they have four sides
　　yellow if they have five sides
　　green if they have six sides.

Name _____

pentagons and hexagons

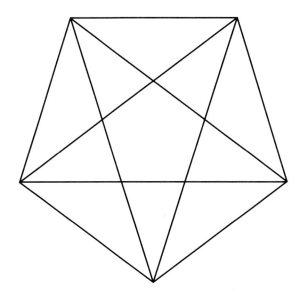

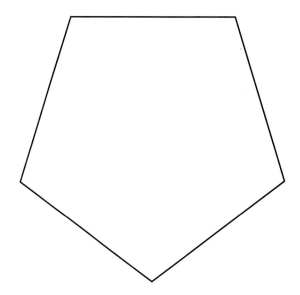

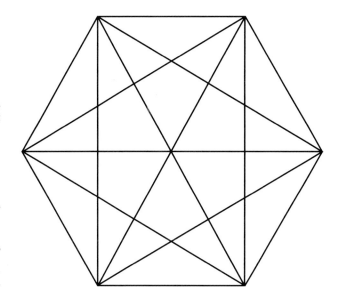

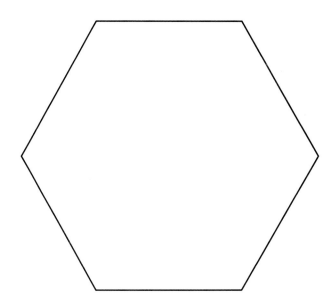

Teacher's instructions
These designs are made by drawing the diagonals on a pentagon and
hexagon.
Colour the regions on the shapes on the left to make patterns.
Draw diagonals on the other shapes and colour them to make patterns.

Name _____

shapes

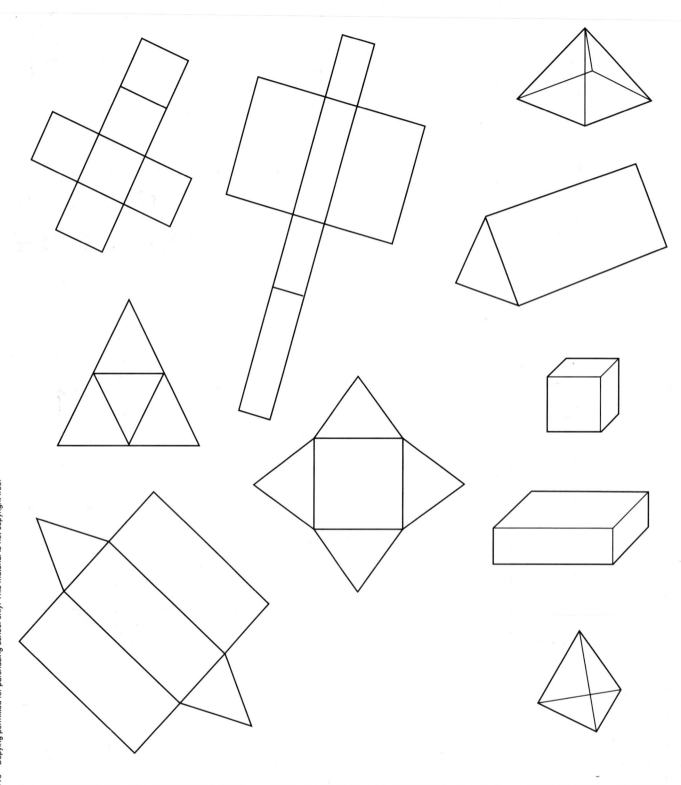

Teacher's instructions
The shapes on the right have been opened out to make the pictures (nets)
on the left.
Colour the matching shapes and nets. Use a different colour for each pair.

73

Name _____

shapes

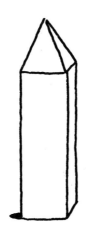

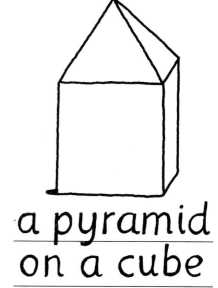

a pyramid
on a cube

_____

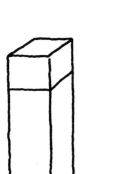

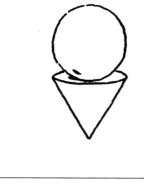

_____

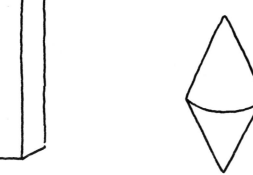

_____

Teacher's instructions
Each picture shows one shape on top of another.
Describe each picture.

Name _____

symmetry

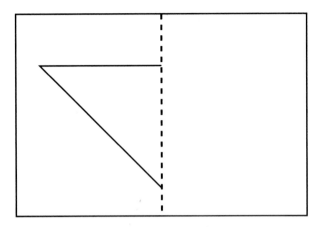

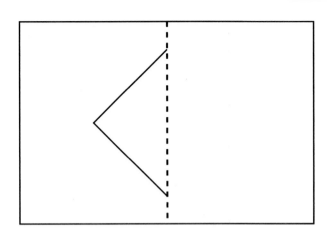

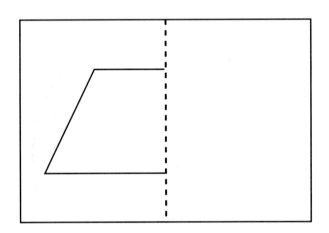

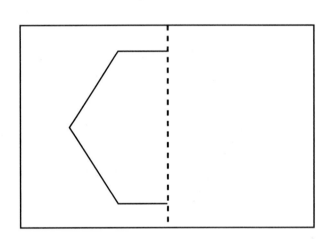

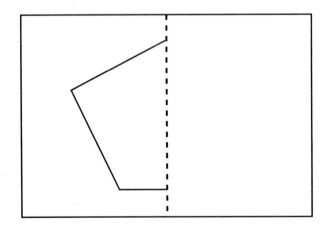

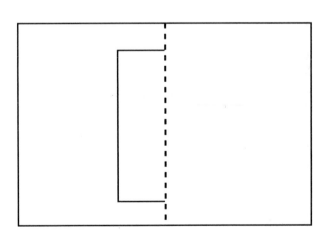

Teacher's instructions
Cut out the six rectangles. Fold each along the fold line.
Guess what shape you will make when you cut out each piece.
Cut out the piece. Open it out.
What shape have you cut? Did you guess correctly?

Materials
Scissors

Name _____

symmetry

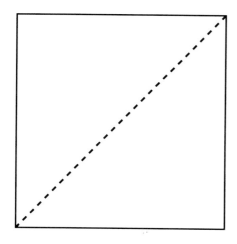

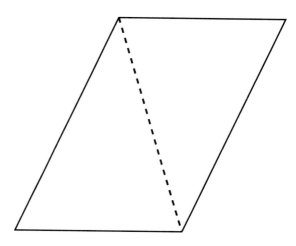

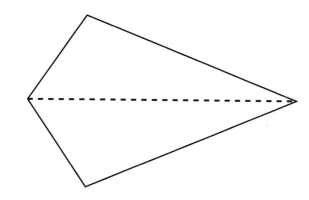

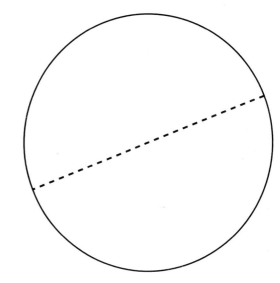

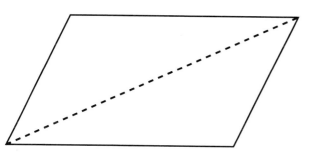

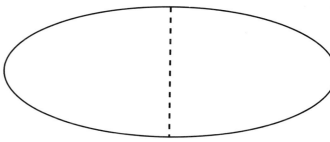

Teacher's instructions
Cut out each shape.
Fold each along the fold line.
Test to see if the folds are lines of symmetry.

Materials
Scissors